THE
Silver Moon

The Power of One
Tandia
April Fool's Day
A Recipe for Dreaming
The Family Frying Pan
The Night Country
Jessica
Smoky Joe's Cafe
Four Fires
Matthew Flinders' Cat
Brother Fish
Whitethorn
Sylvia
The Persimmon Tree
Fishing for Stars
The Story of Danny Dunn
Fortune Cookie
Jack of Diamonds

THE AUSTRALIAN TRILOGY
The Potato Factory
Tommo & Hawk
Solomon's Song

Also available in one volume,
as *The Australian Trilogy*

BRYCE COURTENAY

THE Silver Moon

REFLECTIONS ON LIFE, DEATH AND WRITING

VIKING
an imprint of
PENGUIN BOOKS

VIKING

Published by the Penguin Group
Penguin Group (Australia)
707 Collins Street, Melbourne, Victoria 3008, Australia
(a division of Penguin Australia Pty Ltd)
Penguin Group (USA) Inc.
375 Hudson Street, New York, New York 10014, USA
Penguin Group (Canada)
90 Eglinton Avenue East, Suite 700, Toronto, Canada ON M4P 2Y3
(a division of Penguin Canada Books Inc.)
Penguin Books Ltd
80 Strand, London WC2R 0RL England
Penguin Ireland
25 St Stephen's Green, Dublin 2, Ireland
(a division of Penguin Books Ltd)
Penguin Books India Pvt Ltd
11 Community Centre, Panchsheel Park, New Delhi 110 017, India
Penguin Group (NZ)
67 Apollo Drive, Rosedale, Auckland 0632, New Zealand
(a division of Penguin New Zealand Pty Ltd)
Penguin Books (South Africa) (Pty) Ltd
Rosebank Office Park, Block D, 181 Jan Smuts Avenue, Parktown North, Johannesburg 2196, South Africa
Penguin (Beijing) Ltd
7F, Tower B, Jiaming Center, 27 East Third Ring Road North, Chaoyang District, Beijing 100020, China

Penguin Books Ltd, Registered Offices: 80 Strand, London WC2R 0RL, England

First published by Penguin Group (Australia), 2014

10 9 8 7 6 5 4 3 2 1

Text copyright © Christine Courtenay 2014
Illustrations copyright © Ben Ashton-Bell 2014
Bryce Courtenay's biographical quotations compiled from interviews with Penguin Books and inhouse archives.

Cover design by Alex Ross © Penguin Group (Australia)
Text design by Adam Laszczuk © Penguin Group (Australia)
Illustrations by Ben Ashton-Bell
Cover photography by Comstock/Getty Images
Author photograph by Tim Bauer 2012
Typeset in Adobe Garamond
Printed and bound in China by Everbest Printing Co. Ltd.

National Library of Australia
Cataloguing-in-Publication data:

Courtenay, Bryce, 1933–2012, author.
The silver moon : reflections on life, death and writing /
Bryce Courtenay.
9780670078264
Subjects: Reflections in literature. Life. Death. Writing.

A823.3

penguin.com.au

Bryce Courtenay AM
Writer & Storyteller
1933–2012

'Bryce used to say to me, "The reader is always right".
This beautiful collection of short stories is dedicated to the
millions of readers around the world who loved Bryce,
both for his writing and for the way he lived his life. I know
Bryce would wish us to say to his beloved readers
"Thank you, thank you, thank you".'

CHRISTINE COURTENAY AM (CANBERRA, 2014)

'In the end, if someone says, "Here lies Bryce Courtenay, a storyteller", my life will have been worthwhile.'

THE AGE, JULY 1997

FOREWORD

BRYCE COURTENAY WAS A REMARKABLE MAN in many ways. Australia's most prolific and biggest-selling author for over twenty years, he has sold ten million books in Australia, and millions more around the world in eighteen languages, including Japanese and Chinese.

Bryce was a passionate man, and never so much as when he was engaged in what he liked best – talking about reading and writing. He was an inspirational speaker, whether it was to one person or to an audience, and he made a lasting impression on everyone he met. Still today, almost two years since his death, he has a staggering number of 'likes' on his Facebook page.

His first book, *The Power of One* (1989), was written when

he was fifty-three, and has alone sold over six million copies. It was adapted as a successful film in 1992, starring Morgan Freeman. His last novel, *Jack of Diamonds*, was published in November 2012, and thanks to some speedy work on the part of his printer, he was able to hold a copy in his hands shortly before he died. In between, he wrote, published and promoted an incredible twenty-one books in twenty-three years. He has been likened to a latter-day Charles Dickens, with his sweeping plots, his larger-than-life characters, and his ability to please his readers over and over again.

The story of Bryce's life has the colour of one of his plotlines, Bryce himself one of his largest characters. He was born on 14 August 1933 in a small town in the mountainous Limpopo province of South Africa. Bryce's mother was often visited by a man referred to as his Uncle Arthur, who gave Bryce a copy of *A Writer's Notebook* by W. Somerset Maugham when he was fifteen years old. He was later to discover that this man was in fact his biological father, a fact only revealed to him in the final days of his mother's life.

He learned from a young age the power of words. When he was just five, he was sent to an orphanage cum reform school where he was bullied because of the way he spoke. As a means of defence, Bryce quickly learned the art of storytelling: 'Ach man, I'll tell you a story if you stop beating me . . .' When the danger was past, he would lie on his back, watch the clouds scud by, and dream of being a successful writer.

One day, while recovering from an accident, Bryce, who lived in a world where Afrikaans was the *lingua franca,* came across a beautifully bound book full of English words. He purloined the book and hid it until some time later a sympathetic teacher (to whom he later said he owed a huge debt) came into his life and helped him to learn and appreciate the English language.

Winning a scholarship at the age of eleven to the 'posh' King Edward VII School in Johannesburg, he tried to hide his poverty from the other boys and spent his holidays sleeping on park benches and doing odd jobs. Striking up a friendship with one of his classmates' drivers, Bryce started teaching a small group of local Africans to read and write English. The numbers soon swelled until one day the police raided the school hall. Accusing Bryce and his helpers of being 'communists', the police forced them to leave South Africa. In 1950, at the age of seventeen, Bryce went north to find work in the mines of Rhodesia. The work was hard and dangerous, but he made enough money to head off to England in 1953, where he began to formally pursue a career in words at the London School of Journalism.

While in London, Bryce met and fell head over heels in love with a young Australian woman, Benita Solomon, and a year later, when he had finished his journalism degree, he followed her to the city of her birth, Sydney. The moment he reached Australia, he knew he had found a country he could call home. He arrived in 1958 and in 1959 became an Australian citizen. He married Benita in 1959 and they went on to have three sons, Brett, Adam and Damon.

Unable to get a job as a journalist, he found another way to work with words and landed a position as a junior copywriter with the advertising agency McCann Erickson. Within five years he had become one of Australia's top copywriters, credited with award-winning advertising campaigns that included the 'Louie the Fly' Mortein jingle, high-profile Coca-Cola TV campaigns, the original 'Milky Bar Kid' commercial, and the ALP's 1972 election campaign, 'It's Time', created by a team that included Bryce.

His advertising career was on a steep upward trajectory, taking him from McCann Erickson to J Walter Thompson and eventually on to his own outfit, Harris Robinson Courtenay, which he later sold to George Patterson, becoming its high-profile creative director. By this time, like many ad men, he was working long hours, drinking far too many bottles of wine and smoking too many cigarettes. All at once, Bryce decided that time was short and he needed to 'clean up his act'. As with everything he did, there were no half-measures. He gave up the booze and the cigarettes and took up running – obsessively. Over the next twenty-five years Bryce competed in over forty marathons around the world and, most importantly, he started to write.

Climbing out of bed one morning in 1986, Bryce went to his study and tapped out the words 'This is what happened', so beginning his first novel, *The Power of One*. This was meant to be a 'practice book', and Bryce didn't expect to have anything accepted for publication until his second or third attempt. Instead, the book took one year and two minutes to write, and quickly became a worldwide bestseller, kick-starting his career as a popular novelist.

Around this time, Bryce and Benita's youngest son, Damon, who had been a haemophiliac, was diagnosed with medically acquired HIV, contracted through a blood transfusion. Tragically Damon passed away in 1991 at the age of 24, just two months before *Tandia*, the sequel to *The Power of One*, was published. Bryce had time to dedicate *Tandia* to Damon, and then went on to became an outspoken advocate for the rights of families of people who had passed away from medically acquired HIV.

He sat down to write an incredibly powerful account of the family's experience. *April Fool's Day* (1993), apart from becoming one his most popular books, is credited with helping change public perceptions of AIDS and the treatment of people living with HIV.

Bryce retired from his advertising career to become a full-time writer in 1993, and began researching and writing the first of what became known as his 'Australian trilogy', *The Potato Factory* (1995). He wrote a total of twenty-one books: *The Power of One* (1989), *Tandia* (1992), *April Fool's Day* (1993), *Recipe for Dreaming* (1994), *The Potato Factory* (1995), *The Family Frying Pan* (1997), *Tommo and Hawk* (1997), *Jessica* (1998), *The Night Country* (1998), *Solomon's Song* (1999), *Smoky Joe's Cafe* (2001), *Four Fires* (2001), *Mathew Flinders' Cat* (2002), *Brother Fish* (2004), *Whitethorn* (2005), *Sylvia* (2006), *The Persimmon Tree* (2007), *Fishing for the Stars* (2008), *The Story of Danny Dunn* (2009), *Fortune Cookie* (2010), and *Jack of Diamonds* (2012). In 2001 Bryce was named bestselling Australian author of the decade with the top bestselling novels of the decade being *The Power of One*, *The Potato Factory* and *Jessica*.

Despite his punishing writing regime (he would sometimes write for more than twelve hours straight), Bryce always found time to share his storytelling gifts with writing students around the world. In the year 2000 Bryce conducted a writing course aboard a ship bound for Antarctica, and a final masterclass at the National Library in Canberra just six weeks before he died.

In October 2011 Bryce Courtenay married his soulmate and partner of seven-and-a-half years, Christine Gee. Christine was a pioneer in adventure travel and co-founded Australian Himalayan Expeditions (now World Expeditions), and is also a founding director of the Australian Himalayan Foundation. In addition to being his much-cherished partner in life, Bryce credited Christine with insightful help with his novels, particularly in obscure areas of research and in unravelling plot knots.

Bryce and Christine shared a passion for preserving the world's wildlife and actively supported a range of small NGOs, including Save African Rhino Foundation, and the Thin Green Line Foundation.

Bryce loved to spend time in their beautiful garden in Canberra (it contains flowers and vegetables and is picture perfect) and also with his ever-present pets, Timmy the dog, and four cats: Princess Cardamon, Muschka, Ophelia and Pirate.

This newfound happiness was cut short in 2012 with the diagnosis of terminal stomach cancer (the original cancer had been diagnosed in late 2010 after Bryce had completed a 140-kilometre trek in Kenya). After a brave fight, Bryce passed away in November 2012, at home, with Christine, his family and his beloved pets by his side. A few weeks earlier, his final novel, *Jack of Diamonds*, had been published and quickly became a bestseller.

Throughout his extraordinary career Bryce always put his readers first and used to say 'The reader is always right'. Multi-talented and multi-faceted, Bryce said, 'In the end, if someone says, "Here lies Bryce Courtenay, a storyteller", my life will have been worthwhile.'

Bryce's millions of readers loved him both for his storytelling, and for his approach to life. His enduring legacy is in his many novels and in his generous spirit, which provides a continuing inspiration.

ROBERT SESSIONS AM

LONG-TIME PUBLISHER AND FRIEND OF BRYCE COURTENAY

I was beaten up every day until one day I said,

'Ach man, I'll tell you a story if you stop.'

Then I threatened not to tell them the next

episode if I got beaten up again. It was tough,

but it could have been tougher if I hadn't been

born with blue eyes and white skin.

'Storytellers are the keepers – we are the timekeepers, the continuity keepers. We are the people who tell us who we are, where we've come from, and maybe even where we're going.'

EXCERPT FROM PENGUIN TV INTERVIEW
WITH BRYCE COURTENAY, 2012

THE THINKING WELL

WE ALL NEED A PLACE IN OUR MINDS where we can go to think. A place to sit quietly through a bad patch, regain our equilibrium when things go wrong, work out what path to take when we reach a confusion of crossroads in life. Somewhere to go where we pause to take the spoon out of the sink before we turn on the tap.

In a sense this is a mental sanctuary where we go to review opportunities to be taken or rejected, to sift information, calm fears and subdue that impetuous rush of blood to the head when we've reacted without restraint and humiliated ourselves or unnecessarily castigated or humiliated someone else. Where we decide to make the decision to apologise for our behaviour.

This quiet internal sanctuary is where we more carefully review a decision we feel forced by others to accept or one demanded by a work superior, or a parent, or brought about by peer-group pressure. Where anger or hurt slowly melts and calm and reason seeps steadily and meaningfully into our consciousness. Somewhere we can go to examine pointless pride and give ourselves permission to feel regret and courage – and by so doing dissolve the angst and resentment that causes the confusion we've built up in hearts and minds.

This process is not spiritual. It is not meditation. There is no 'Ummm' sound in the background, no yellow-robed shaven-headed priests or temple bells tinkling in the wind. Instead, this is the simple joy and gratifying task of thinking in a surrounding we know or imagine or recall from the past. A place to go sometimes literally but usually in our imaginations while seated quietly in a chair, arms resting palms placed flat onto our knees or hands softly folded into our laps. Here we commence the process of talking to ourselves, or formulate necessary imaginative conversations with others.

This thinking citadel should not be seen as the usual 'grab-bag' thinking, the snatching at thoughts on the run with a passing referral to experience or consequence. It is, instead, somewhat deeper, a sorting of thoughts – call it mental rummaging. Not always tidy, it's the paraphernalia of what we know, what we yet need to learn, what we need to consign to the garbage or retain for future use.

Calm anger, reasoned regret, appropriate happiness and self-confidence are what we retain. Envy, greed or a sense of entitlement is to be tossed away as the detritus that prevents clear thinking.

Everything we say and do has a consequence, small or large, good or bad. Try to ask yourself, 'If I win this argument I'm about to provoke, will it change anything?' If the chances of a positive outcome exist then go calmly for the point you wish to make, and accept that your opponent's opinion may also be valid. 'A man convinced against his will is of the same opinion still.'

Without understanding and, as well, anticipating the consequences of our actions, we are leading lives based more or less on guesswork, on happenstance. In effect we are largely knee-jerking to the stimulus other people hurl at us. Rather than working steadily and progressively towards the achievement of an ambition or an immediate goal, we are placing ourselves in the hands of a potentially lesser self, hoping, almost by chance, for the right outcome. Your own wisdom should not be downplayed, underestimated or needlessly dismissed but it should always be tested. The same applies to the wisdom of others, which is not necessarily superior to your own.

Common sense is not the prerogative of the few. Instead it is the trial and error of our everyday lives, the accumulation of experience and the sifting-out of past negative outcomes. Do the sifting in your head, use what you know from your own achievements and what you may gain from observing others. By all means borrow, but do not replicate – one size does not fit all – improve, alter, adjust. In thought nothing is perfectly wrought, thinking is a moving feast and circumstances tend to change with every repast.

To do your thinking you may want to recall a place where you were supremely happy and contented and felt completely safe, or you may imagine an entirely original thinking site.

Wherever your thinking location, it is important to remember it is *your* location entirely – a place in your head where you go alone, where the words and thoughts and deeds of others can only be given admission on your own terms. People you may want to address, or from whom you wish to seek advice, are only permitted to enter your personal space in your imagination and only after you have agreed (in your imagination) to allow them to enter. This is *your* location where you go to unknot the jumbled complexities we all encounter in the increasingly discombobulated world we share with others.

Having located the thinking site in your imagination, here then is how you go about travelling to it in reality. Count backwards from one hundred as you journey to your secret mind place, stop counting when you've reached it and emptied your head of the where, what, how and when of the moment, then introduce the subject about which you need to think.

However, and this is important, do your thinking in the personal pronoun. In your private space the word 'I' is essential. Do the 'I' examination: Ask yourself, 'How do *I* feel about this situation? What outcome do *I* want to achieve? How do *I* bring this about? What do *I* need to do to change? Am *I* responsible for this? Do *I* accept responsibility? Do *I* act (accept the leadership or speak out) when everyone else is scared to do so? Do *I* need to give up this or that bad habit to succeed and do *I* want to do so sufficiently to achieve my objective? Am *I* being a bastard/bitch? Is what *I* am doing fair? Am *I* cheating? How will *I* benefit from this decision? Am *I* being greedy at the expense of others? Is the benefit *I* receive worth the action(s) involved? Should *I* be doing this to make others around me happy? What can *I* do today that positively affects someone else's life, and so becomes a shared happiness?

There are many more questions you will ask of yourself, although I feel sure you get the general idea.

These questions asked to yourself, decided upon and then acted upon, will in almost every case lead on to fame and fortune or, more importantly, happiness and contentment. With a little practice, this process of reasoned thinking will become a natural part of your life. You will find that five minutes or so is about all you can sustain at first. Later this time will increase. If sometimes you should fall asleep that too is good for you. Thinking is a learning process and well worth time and concentration. If you decide to use just ten minutes a day (no more than twenty is ever required) to arm your daily endeavour with conscious thought and decisive direction, you will be enormously gratified at the results you achieve.

Being a curious kid, I looked into the
packing case and saw it was full of
books — books written in English. Now this
was Boer country where you weren't allowed
to speak English, but on top I saw the most
beautiful thing I'd ever seen. Bound in Morocco
leather was a book with gold-edged pages,
and it had a bit of filigree on it. It was the
only thing I've ever stolen in my life.

'Unless we teach our children to forage for information and that words and wisdom are inside a book, unless they become literate, they cannot become the thinkers and dreamers that we are going to require to be a young and splendid nation.'

THE AUSTRALIAN, NOVEMBER 1996

WHERE THE GIRAFFE
COMES TO DRINK FROM THE
SILVER BOWL OF THE MOON

I WAS BORN IN AFRICA and as a small boy of seven was placed in a hostel for boys deep in the rural north of Southern Africa. The Boys Hostel was a horrid, lonely place, where I was constantly bullied for somehow being different, though quite why was a mystery but most definitely had something to do with the terrible fact that I didn't have a roll of skin covering the top of my penis, that I had been circumcised.

Of course, I had no idea that this was a deliberate act of man and not a birth blemish. As far as I knew this hatless penis was almost certainly a deformity and one that I was constantly reminded was most definitely a punishment from God.

When things got too bad for me to endure I'd walk along a game track that began in the thorn scrub not far from the hostel and I'd go and sit on a big grey rock some distance away. It was a place nobody else ever came, a place I had to myself. The rock overlooked a soak, a small drinking hole, where the smallest game, a warthog, tiny antelope or any number of shy, usually unnoticed, lesser wild creatures, moles, pygmy hedgehogs, bush mice, lizards and birds came to drink. On one such occasion when I'd taken my small-boy misery to the rock an event occurred that was to change my life forever.

It was towards the end of the dry season before the rains come, when the soak this late in summer still held a little muddy water at its centre. Close to sunset I sat quietly blubbing. I was aware that bawling was against the rules – any form of crying was not allowed at the Boys Hostel – but here nobody could see me so I allowed myself a self-indulgent sob or two before I said my daily prayer to ask God to forgive whatever sin it was that I'd committed and please, please, to grow the skin hat I needed to cover my shame and so make me the same as everyone else. Having completed these two daily rituals I sat quietly to watch the waterhole. Small creatures approaching water are hesitant and look every which way before taking each tentative step, aware that sudden disaster in the form of a predator could appear from anywhere.

The day was beginning to shut down in a fiery blaze of tangerine-coloured sunlight. This is the last time the small and the vulnerable have an opportunity to have a drink before the dark and dangerous cloak of night descends.

With the sun beginning to set it became time for me to depart, and all I'd seen was a lone male warthog. The warthog, true to its name, is a small black pig-like animal with curved white tusks that curl over his snout to almost touch and resemble a huge, dirty white moustache. Together with a dotting of hairy moles on his snout he gives the appearance of an exceedingly grumpy old man. Thick rough hair redolent of a black jacket reaches down to cover his neck, shoulders and halfway down his back, to leave his tummy and bottom bare and hairless but for a short tufted tail that sticks bolt upright. To all appearances he looks as if he has put on his Sunday-best jacket but then left home in a terrible snorting huff, quite forgetting in the furore to pull on his trousers.

I liked seeing warthogs because they made me laugh, but then also caused me to have a bit of a second sniff, because, just as God had forgotten to give me a hat for my penis, He'd also forgotten to give the warthog a nice pair of trousers to go with his jacket. Can you imagine how tough this was for him? You see, I only got laughed at in the showers when everyone would form a circle around me to see my hatless you-know-what. If I covered it with both hands two of the bigger boys would force my arms behind my back or I'd get a whack across the head that made my eyes water (remember you're not allowed to cry). But then again, if I'd been born a warthog I'd be walking around all over the place without my pants on. There's always somebody who's worse off than you are.

In the African bush darkness follows sunset alarmingly quickly, and I didn't want to be caught on foot in the period of darkness before the moon rose. Then, just as night was about to catch me napping, from behind a whitethorn tree a giraffe emerged. Wow! It moved towards the muddy waterhole in its spectacular long stilt-legged yet perfectly coordinated and seemingly effortless manner, it's tail like a great fly switch swinging from side to side. In the fast-gathering dark I could hear the swish of the parting scrub and the clatter of loose pebbles as it approached the small puddle at the centre of the almost dry soak.

Game other than elephant and lion always approach water cautiously and I knew that the giraffe might take some time before it decided to drink. In other words, making sure that it didn't place itself in a position where it would be vulnerable to a predator, though its only danger was from a pride of lions hunting together, and I'd never seen any such near the Boys Hostel – although I don't suppose the giraffe knew this.

Wisdom dictated I should leave at once, that I'd get the *sjambok* for staying out after dark. While I knew the beautiful creature wouldn't harm me, I remained on the big rock frozen in anticipation lest I be the one to deny it a drink. Besides, the temptation to stay became too great to resist.

I told myself it was a full moon that night and if I waited out the ten or fifteen minutes of darkness before it rose I would easily locate the game path back to the Boys Hostel in the moonlight. The full moon would bathe the bush in a rich silver light so I'd be able to see clear as anything. I watched the sun set and waited out the frightening minutes of darkness and then, with more than a small sigh of relief, finally saw a curved sliver of moon appear over the dark and distant horizon.

In this part of Africa the moon rises almost as quickly as the sun sets. In what seemed less than ten minutes the bush was bathed in moonlight, turning the giraffe from a silhouette to its brick-brown crazy-patterned skin with each irregular brown shape placed in a soft saffron surround.

It too had waited for the moon to rise, for it now stood at the very edge of the dry circle of clay some four metres from the tiny muddy pond at the centre of the soak. Then, seemingly as if in slow motion, its front legs collapsed like a folding chair and its enormous torso came to rest on the dry, cracked clay surrounding the splash of late summer water. As a final caution, its neck swung in a wide arc across the breadth of the waterhole to the bush beyond. Then, at the very moment its towering neck lowered and its head came to rest above the water, the reflection of the moon appeared on the surface of the tiny pond and the tallest of all the great beasts drank from the silver bowl of the moon.

Forever since, when I go to think, I go to the place where the giraffe comes to drink from the silver bowl of the moon.

It was the first time I'd been shown any kindness.
I asked her to teach me to read. By the time I was
twelve I had memorised that book. The point is
I fell in love with words — the power of words.
What words could actually do to a person.
After she left, Miss Bornstein wrote to me every
month and sent me three books and a little exam
paper on what was in them. When I was eleven,
Miss Bornstein said I should sit for a scholarship
for a very posh school in Johannesburg.
She said it was unlikely I would pass but it
would be good practice for the following year.
Well I sat the exam and passed. I won the
scholarship. Without her I wouldn't be here
today; she changed everything for me.

'Kindness to me is a very important idea. We always talk about love, but kindness requires more than love; it requires thinking, it requires "What can I do for this person that may not be important to me but may be terribly important to them?" – or maybe it isn't important to them, maybe they've just had a shitty day and somebody comes along and says, "It's going to be okay, it's going to be okay."'

EXCERPT FROM PENGUIN TV INTERVIEW
WITH BRYCE COURTENAY, 2012

TIMMY: THE DOG OF DOGS

WE HAVE FOUR CATS AND A DOG you now know as Timmy. The cats, with the exception of Princess Cardamon, a vastly obese lilac Burmese, all found their own way unannounced into our home. But Timmy's entry into our lives was somewhat different.

Some eleven years ago I owned seventy acres in a lovely valley inland from the Central Coast of New South Wales and on my way to it one morning I passed a cattle property run by a guy named Rick Stackman. Rick was a big-mouthed know-all, but he knew cattle and also bred a crossbreed of cattle dog for which he was justly famous. His dogs, a mixture of kelpie, border collie and blue heeler, were much in demand. But, on this particular morning as

I passed his farm gate I saw that he was in the process of wringing the neck of a puppy who seemed no older than three or four months.

I stopped with the proverbial squeal of brakes, "Rick, stop!" I yelled at the big man.

'No fucking good, mate,' Stockman shouted back. 'I just put him in with a mob of cows and he's got himself stomped half t' fuckin' death. Never gunna make it as a cattle dog, useless little fucker . . . better off dead.'

I fished out a fifty-dollar note and demanded the pup.

'You're a bloody idiot, Bryce, his nose is broken and his spine crushed – I'd be taking your money, mate.'

'Rick, I *want* that pup!'

'Righto, don't say I didn't tell yiz . . . Be better dead, mate,' he repeated, handing over the whimpering little fellow and accepting the fifty bucks.

I took the pup directly to the vet in Peats Ridge, where he remained for three weeks and two operations, but finally made it home.

We now live in Canberra and every evening I take the now aging Timmy Courtenay up to the sports oval where he meets a dozen or so of his friends for a bum-sniff hello, tail-wagging romp together with a modicum of ball chasing. I count myself fortunate that their collective owners have become my friends as well.

Timmy's puppy experience is beginning to show – he has arthritis, limps a bit and is getting slower by the day. He sleeps in a large basket on the carpet at the foot of my bed and snores like a chainsaw at night. But life without Timmy Courtenay would not be quite the same lovely experience. Even the cats tolerate him – all but Muschka, who only just accepts him, but then she's got a few attitude problems of her own and doesn't like to shower too much praise about, especially for a canine. Although I think she sort of mothers him in her own strange way. 'Piss off, darl' is her favourite expression when he approaches. But at least it's not said with a fangs-showing hiss.

'Reading became my life, my absolute life. It got me
a scholarship to a posh school; it got me a scholarship
to an overseas university; it got me into life . . . it did
it all for me.'

WEST AUSTRALIAN, NOVEMBER 1996

Boarding school was very difficult. I was with
the sons of millionaires and I was a popular kid,
but life was fraught with this need for money and
never showing I was poor. I ended up playing
rugby for the school and was a good sportsman,
but I felt like a nobody. I lived with this
ambivalence all the time. I couldn't tell anyone
at school I was illegitimate so I invented parents
who had died in a mysterious accident.

'When we teach our children a respect for language,
the kind it takes to turn them into readers, we give them
the basic building blocks of creativity, the disciplines
required to think widely, seek information and effectively
articulate and communicate with others.'

THE BULLETIN, OCTOBER 1997

I BELIEVE THIS

WE ARE TOLD THAT OUR BELIEF SYSTEMS are usually inculcated in childhood, some negative, others positive, so that parents and institutions – religious and others – are responsible for what we believe as adults. The influences on my young life were a mixture of all of these. I was born illegitimately, or to use the common euphemism, to a single parent. This involved some time spent in an orphanage and some with a mother prone to nervous breakdowns, who had embraced a charismatic religion. Finally, at the age of eleven, I received a scholarship to a boys' school closely patterned on the English public school system.

Putting all this together as the bunch of influences

that formed my character, it may be said that I was lonely, frequently bullied, and often whipped, trusted few adults, and soon realised that institutions regarded anyone who appeared to be an individual or clever with great suspicion; sadness was a common emotion. Furthermore, I knew at an early age that I was a sinner and therefore filled with guilt and would need to be saved by being born again. To round things off, I was influenced by the teachings of a bigoted, supposed racially superior, white male supremacist, upper-class South African boys' boarding school. Taking all these things into consideration there seemed little room for a positive belief system to emerge.

However, my first belief is that we are responsible for ourselves. A teacher once informed me that the best helping hands you are ever likely to experience are attached to your wrists. I became a very competent boxer so that any bigger boy taking me on soon knew I was no pushover. I was said to be very bright, but I think it was more that I refused to give up; in the end it was persistence more than anything that won the day. I decided that between the Dutch Reformed Church (orphanage), the Apostolic Faith Mission (parent) and the Church of England (boarding school) it was probably a good idea to fashion my own sense of God – someone who expects me to exercise the more noble aspects of humanity and who doesn't wish to be constantly bothered with the things in life I ought to be able to take care of myself.

This was all very well, but it didn't quite take care of my low self-esteem, an almost inevitable result of the childhood I had lived. I decided to hide this sense of inadequacy, and there are two places where a child can safely do this. The first is to merge with the crowd, to become nothing in particular, neither noticed nor noted. Dead average is always a safe hiding place. The second is way up front, the 'catch me if you can' position. And so I tried my best to excel, to use to the full extent what small gifts I had been given. In the process I developed a mantra for my life, which goes like this:

When you're skating on thin ice, you may as well tap dance.

I also think of it as 'the power of one', that ability we all have to overcome the negative influences in out lives and to finally triumph without having to become a bastard; to spit in the face of adversity and circumstance and to refuse to be beaten by either or both.

These days spontaneous kindness is looked upon as a need to be loved by everyone; charity is seen as a manifestation of guilt; happiness is regarded as a lack of intelligence and even pity has to be carefully qualified to receive the approbation of one's peer group. At the age of six I recall being made to learn, by shouting out by rote, what my kindergarten teacher at the time termed 'Our very nice saying':

> I shall pass through this world but once,
> Any good thing I can do, or any kindness I can show
> To any fellow human being . . . let me do it now,
> For I shall not pass this way again.

It is hardly appropriate in today's cynical world, but after all the effort I've put into life, I have come to the conclusion that 'Our very nice saying' is what I believe life is intrinsically all about.

PUBLISHED IN *I BELIEVE THIS*, EDITED BY JOHN MARSDEN (RANDOM HOUSE AUSTRALIA, 2004)

I had no money, so I had to get a job to pay for my school uniforms . . . I started to teach a small group of Africans to read and write . . . One day the hall was raided by the police, who branded me a communist because they considered educating black Africans a subversive act. A police chief wrote me a note encouraging me to leave, saying that if I came back he'd place me under house arrest.

'Keep a diary. You might think you can remember what it's like in thirty years time, but you can't. But if it's in the diary . . . it's your emotional self.'

WESTERN ADVOCATE, APRIL 1994

MUSCHKA: THE NEEDY ONE

IF MUSCHKA THE CAT were to be personified you'd recognise her immediately. She's the scrawny lady in her early forties you invariably see shopping in the mall who wears an orange tracksuit, clean but not new, thongs in the summer, cheap runners in the winter. Her hair is always short, badly cut and unnaturally blonde and in need of a touch-up at the dark roots. She wears a smudge of lipstick, the colour clashing with her tracksuit, and her face has been exposed to too much sun so that premature aging is already apparent around her eyes. She seems never without a cigarette drooping from the right-hand corner of her mouth and it's difficult to decipher the colour of her eyes as she squints from the twirl of rising blue smoke when she looks up.

She refers to both genders as 'darl' and doesn't take any shit from anyone and tells it how it is – or rather, how she perceives it to be. Any psychologist will tell you she's looking for love but has given up thinking she may ever find it. Also that she secretly feels deeply inadequate and uses her tough outward demeanour to conceal her inner needs. She commences getting pissed around five at night with her first glass of 'Sav B' tapped from a cardboard cask.

If you've come across her when in the supermarket then translate her into a feline and you've got Muschka Courtenay, the needy one – the cat that came in from the rain and the cold and the dangerous bush.

I first saw Muschka while taking Timmy for our morning walk up into the hills some two kilometres away from the farm, when I noticed two sharp green eyes appeared in the undergrowth beside the overgrown pathway.

Tim will run for his life at the mere sight of a cow or a horse and he loves to chase wallabies and wild goats, and I could hear him barking in the distance, displaying (ha ha) the so-called macho side of his character.

I knew at once that the pair of eyes peering at me did not belong to a genuine feral cat, as they are much too wary to show themselves. This was probably a cat that had lost its owners. So I 'puss-puss'd' for a few moments before moving away in the direction of Timmy's excited barking, aware that a domestic cat can roam up to ten kilometres from its home. The following day I left a tin of cat food beside the path where I'd seen the eyes. On our return from our walk it had been eaten. This was definitely a lost cat in the process of going feral.

I repeated the cat food every day for at least a month, calling 'puss-puss' and placing the food a few hundred metres closer to my farm gate each morning. Standing fifty or so metres away I'd wait and she'd soon appear to gulp down the gift of food.

Eventually I drew the shabby, scrawny little grey cat to the gate. It took another two weeks with her hiding among the agapanthus in the garden before one wild and stormy night I passed the front door and saw two little eyes peering hopefully through the glass. I opened the door a crack and left it ajar. The thunderstorm lasted all night and by morning the little cat was nowhere to be seen. Then a little later when I went upstairs to my study to start my day's writing I discovered a very wet, bedraggled little cat cowering under my desk.

Muschka has never left me since, and sits on my lap or on my desk all day as I write. If any of the other cats – Cardamon, Ophelia (Philly) and Pirate – should decide to approach us while 'we're' writing, she arches her back and snarls and hisses. "He's mine, piss off!" she snaps, in a distinctly lower-class cat-cent.

I must say the other three cats take absolutely no notice and she fools no one, though, as I said somewhere else, she tolerates Timmy, calls him 'darl', accepting his presence at my feet as part of the essential writing team, even though I suspect she's illiterate.

I know she loves me to bits. Although, if I don't stroke her in her needy moments, which are frequent, she reaches up and gives me a whack on the jaw, though I must say never exposing a deadly claw.

One thing I have to say in her favour is that she's got a lot of internal fortitude. On one occasion the neighbour's rottweiler ventured into the garden while Muschka, as ever, was tailing me. His name is Rocky and he's not a very nice dog. Not as bad as the reputation his breed enjoys, just . . . well, not nice. Timmy is terrified of him and, seeing him approach cowered beside me, his ears flattened, while his warning to me of the approaching presence of the unwelcome visitor more closely resembled a whimper than a protective growl.

Suddenly the rottweiler let out a frightened yelp then turned and took off, fleeing for its life, his tail so far between his legs he was practically using the tip to inadvertently clean his teeth. Mounted astride his neck was Muschka, her claws digging fiercely into either side of Rocky the Rottweiler's jowls. This is a cat that takes no crap when it comes to protecting a loved one, and I feel pretty sure Timmy, the Dog of Dogs, is secretly counted but never openly admitted to be on this very selective list.

'I love the idea of the way Australia started, of doing it tough. And the way Australia punches above its weight, the way it's been kicked in the arse from the very beginning. It's the only country where you're entitled to reinvent yourself.'

NOVEL LIVES: LEGENDS OF THE WRITTEN WORD
(AUSTRALIA POST, 2010)

Everything about Australia was right; the sky was high, the land and people felt familiar. From day one I felt like an Australian. I remember we came through the Heads and that was it. The sun was shining, with the Harbour like a millpond. Then we could see land and I noticed a white house with a splash of bougainvillea. I immediately thought, I want to own that house. And seventeen years later, I did.

'If a country doesn't have writers it is in a dangerous position – it loses its soul, it loses its personality, it loses those things that make it absolutely unique. In other words, the politicians get in control and that voice singing in the dark is not there. We have to have the voices. Whether they be songs and lyrics or whether they be writing. Writing to my mind is the single most important vocation that we have in any country.'

EXCERPT FROM *THE LAST CLASS* DVD, 2012

WORDS

I GUESS AS A WRITER I care about words more than most and while it's natural that the new technology such as Facebook and Twitter and the by now almost universally used email encourages us to use a bunch of words that are colourless and often cut to verbal ribbons – 'How R U', 'Luv U' or similar – it seems to be a process that is squeezing the life out of language.

I am aware that language is a constantly changing medium – new words and forms arrive, old ones die out. Like life, a great many common words have a brief lifespan before passing away. But English is a beautiful and expressive language that more than most languages can explain through idiom our society to ourselves.

Truncating words into small, common, lifeless little objects, meaningless phrases as if what we have to say and therefore we ourselves are unimportant and worthless seems to me to be a tragic transgression into nowhere. Someone once said we are known by the words we use.

Allow me to talk a little about words, those lovely, jumping, laughing, eager little marks we make on paper or tap onto a screen.

Words gather around a proposition or an idea or story willingly. Some wag their tails, others stand back a little shy, but they've come to work, some shuffle as they stand in line, others stand to rigid attention while you can almost hear some of them tap dancing. But the big ones and the small ones, the extroverted words and the shy words all want to be part of the action, part of your narrative. They all want to get into the act, all are anxious to make your writing just the very best it can be.

If you love words they force you to use them intelligently, they don't merely want to show off – in fact, they love working hard. Nothing echoes more loudly than a hollow word or lacks meaning as does a lazy one.

Some words run softly, on tippy-toe, almost soundless, others clump around like an under-fourteen football team milling around on the cement floor of the dressing shed. Some soothe like cold cream on sunburn while others can set your blood pounding. Expletives are a part of our language and they too can be used well or simply wasted, thrown together in a sentence to denote little but an inability to think or pause meaningfully in an attempt to find an appropriate adjective.

There are words so rounded at the edges and softened by wear that they are no longer words at all but the sounds that people make for confusion, despair, joy or anger. There are words that are randy (old-fashioned word) or sexy but not dirty or foul. And sacred words that have become expletives, their meanings soiled with improper, unthinking and careless use.

Some words stick like burrs and punish at a touch. They are words we never forget, insults and denigrating words that destroy our egos and sometimes even our lives.

But then there are also words that nurse the ego and heal the heart.

There are words joined together in common phrases we barely notice as we employ them in everyday use, yet if you pause a moment to think, they are so beautiful that they elevate the human race. For instance, here is a phrase so common we use it without a moment's thought, yet it is a miracle of invention. How it ever came into being is a marvel and a mystery. Who was it to first use our language with such finesse? The phrase: 'Beyond

41

a shadow of a doubt.' Just pause for a moment. *Beyond* meaning a way ahead, *a shadow* a dark area covering light, *a doubt*, a hesitancy in belief. How blithely we employ this phrase, yet how exquisitely beautiful it is in its thought and structure. Our language contains hundreds, perhaps thousands of similar miracles of expression that lead to deeper understanding or emphasis.

Though there are also phrases that clunk, or do for me. Here is one, 'I mean this from the bottom of my heart.' In my mind's eye I see a heart with a large bottom and anything, even a sentiment, coming from it is not to be trusted. Any person 'heart bottoming' me is suspect.

There are also phrases that smack you in the mouth. 'He was found stone cold dead.' Whack!

There are even some words that remain forever unspoken, clamped in a throat that aches to let them out . . . and often they are the most meaningful words of all.

Words are the most of what we have to solve just about everything. The new social media is the most powerful medium for words ever invented. It means you can possess an opinion that can reach around the world without the media or the government putting a spin to it. Your opinion coupled with countless others can stop wars and destroy tyrants. Use it, and if you choose the right words, inequity and hardship – even poverty – can be solved forever.

The choice is ours, words spoken, on the screen, recorded, written, lyrics. If we use them well and care how we put them together, if we think before we open our mouths, tap the computer keys or unclip a pen or compose a lyric or write a poem or even a note to the supermarket, we will do more than simply rescue language, we will begin to communicate meaningfully to with each other as a collective force that can't be stopped. When we talk with purpose and pleasure to each other in this marvellous language we have been given as our birthright then anything is possible and most of it will be very good.

You are a person with a point of view that counts – use it! Find the right words and change the world.

'The books that have shaped me? Hans Christian Andersen's fairy tales, *Peter Pan* by J.M. Barrie, *The Pearl* by John Steinbeck, *Oliver Twist* by Charles Dickens, *King Solomon's Mines* by H. Rider Haggard, *To Kill a Mockingbird* by Harper Lee, *Catch 22* by Joseph Heller, *Love in the Time of Cholera* by Gabriel García Márquez and *Birdsong* by Sebastian Faulks.'

FROM PENGUIN BOOKS' ARCHIVES

I landed a job as a junior copywriter at McCann Erickson. The American agencies had started this idea of having specialist writers who actually wrote material. I didn't know much about advertising but I could write, and I was fortunate to gain experience as a young copywriter in this huge, vast international agency [McCann Erickson].

'Words to me are alive. Some are shy, some are happy, some apprehensive. I hold them in my hands and shudder with anticipation – they are all there for me to use. But they obey me and seem to be happy doing it.'

WEST AUSTRALIAN, JUNE 1991

THIS TALK IS ABOUT WORDS

THIS TALK IS ABOUT WORDS. About loving, touching, reaching out and grabbing copywriter words. Words that spread as smoothly as whipped cream on a silk bedspread. And words that jab hard and suddenly, leaving your lip stinging and your head ringing. Words with big, round, soft, open vowels. And words with tight, hurtful little arseholes. Like 'sneak'.

New York ad people are fond of claiming that the best copywriters come from where the vowels are broad and the broads are loud. It could also be true that here in Australia the best copywriters come from playing cricket on the pavement rather than the playing fields of Cranbrook or Melbourne Grammar.

Australia's earliest settlers, unlike their American counterparts who left England to the promise of a richer and freer existence, were dragged kicking and screaming from the dungeons of Newgate to the living death of an isolated and barren land. They had no time to check a copy of whatever the equivalent of *Fowler's Modern English Usage* was at the time. Their language bore the marks of shackles and carried the inflection of the shanty Irish. And it matured in a harsh land with few niceties, so that little white pantaloons do not belong on the end of an Australian lamb chop.

Our language is laconic and often recalcitrant but it has a blunt vigour, a lust for life that is not being included in much of our work. While we suffer from the 'English disease' in our layouts with pictures and type neat and arranged and prissy as an English garden, we cannot blame the Poms for the language of our advertising. The limp words that fall joylessly onto the page like cold spaghetti. Frantic words that soil white space. Sycophantic, self-indulgent matey words that plop into headlines like fat grey groups. They are all our own work.

We use words as though they were unimportant people – and they are not. They are very important people indeed. If you can get them on your side they will take you everywhere.

Let me put it to you this way. If you love words, if you try to use them well and treat them right, if you respect their function, if you can see their colour and feel their texture, if you understand their constraints, if you know their weaknesses and are aware of their strengths, then you simply cannot write a bad ad.

Let me tell you about words. Words are, in the final sense, all we've got. Words are the beginning of most communication's joy and the root of most of its evil. Man's greatest inheritance has been the gift of speech. Not only because it allowed him to understand, but also because it could put pictures into his mind. The gift of speech is simultaneously the gift of imagination. And it all begins with words.

Advertising is largely the business of words. Yet every day in every agency in this big country there are copywriters and art directors who grab handfuls of words and carelessly bundle them together with baling wire and lay them out in small heaps of semantic garbage across a field of pristine white paper.

Words are most of what advertising has to use. Words on paper, words on tape, words as lyrics, words as captions. It is very rare indeed to find an advertising picture that does not need to lean a little or a lot on words. It is damn near impossible to find one that is worth a thousand good words . . .

If I am beginning to sound a little precious about words, let me dispel very quickly the belief that advertising is an art form in itself. Of all the asinine beliefs that we carry around in our mental grab bag, this little gem has the greatest basic flaw. Advertising is not, nor ever will be, an art form answerable only to itself. Advertising is a commercial subdivision of two basic human skills: communication and persuasion.

Advertising communicates not when copywriters and art directors have satisfied their basic urges. Advertising communicates only when people see a self-interest in reading it, or viewing it, or listening to it. And advertising persuades only when people see a self-interest in doing what you want them to do. Advertising is no more an art form in itself than the frame is around a picture.

EDITED EXCERPT FROM A PAPER PRESENTED BY
BRYCE COURTENAY AT THE 1980 CAXTON AWARDS

There I was, working too hard, drinking too
hard, smoking about a hundred cigarettes
a day and I realised I was looking like a typical
slob executive. Not only that, I had become
involved with a career and forgot about
my lifelong ambition to be a novelist.
Thirty-five years had gone by and I was
most likely to be dead in five years.
So I changed everything.

'All effective writing is re-writing. There are very few geniuses who can transcribe what is in their head directly as finished copy on to the page. Culling, cutting, rethinking, juxtaposing and re-arranging are the very basics of writing.'

THE AGE, OCTOBER 2003

THE DOORSTOP

I'M NOT ONE WHO EXPECTS THINGS to come easily and when, at fifty-three years of age, I decided to attempt to fulfil a lifetime ambition to become a fiction writer I didn't dare hang up my boots in advertising. As it was compulsory that I retire at the age of sixty, as was customary at that time, this gave me five to seven years to get underway.

I telexed every creative director in the eighty-strong worldwide Bates advertising agency network to ask each one to let me know the number of novels the leading fiction writers in their country completed before they were published. After I'd crunched the numbers it turned out to be the fourth.

I decided that I would do the same. I gave myself five

years in which to write four novels. The first three would be practice books I'd complete in exactly a year each (you have to have a deadline); the fourth novel, the one that would hopefully be published, I'd lavish with attention over a period of two years. Cheeky, I know, but there you go – you have to have a dream.

So, I climbed out of bed early one morning in 1986, headed to my study and began what was to become *The Power of One*. 'This is what happened' seemed a good place to start, and I wrote about what I knew – growing up in South Africa. I'd had to pull myself up by the bootstraps, so I believe in the capacity of every human being to triumph and to achieve anything. Peekay, being a fictional character, is larger than life. While there is some crossover in his story and mine, he is a better character than I ever was.

I completed my first practice book in one year and two minutes. While I was on deadline, it didn't occur to me to show it to anyone – my wife included. The kitchen screen door had been banging annoyingly all year, so I tied what amounted to a fairly hefty manuscript with heavy twine and used it as a doorstop. The following night I started the second 'practice' book. By the way, the doorstop worked brilliantly.

Almost a year later, with my second book almost completed, a friend mentioned to Jill Hickson, then one of

Sydney's leading literary agents, that I had written a novel. I guess Jill must have concluded that as an advertising copywriter I might have a flair for words, and she phoned to ask if she could see the manuscript.

'No, no!' I cried. 'It's a practice book – I've used it as the doorstop.' I then explained my five-year plan and promised her the fourth book. 'It'll be good, I promise,' I added, somewhat arrogantly.

'No, please, send me the doorstop,' she urged.

'It's a thousand pages, all brown and badly battered, ma'am,' I protested. 'Certainly it's not worth making a clean copy.' This was all before the advent of the desktop printer, and printing my doorstop would take a couple of hours to complete on the office copy machine.

'Can you send me the manuscript just as it is? I'd really like to read it,' she urged.

A few days later Jill called to say she loved the story. She told me she was soon to attend the American Booksellers Association annual conference, and wanted to take my manuscript with her. To encourage me to agree, she said, 'I'll have a clean copy made at my own expense, Bryce.'

That clinched it for me. I warned her again not to be too hopeful and reiterated my offer to give her my fourth book. 'I'm sure it will be worth the wait as I think I'm slowly getting the hang of this novel-writing business,' I urged, dropping into my accustomed advertising selling mode. In truth, I was beginning to despair. Writing competent fiction was proving no easy task even for a so-called top advertising copy bloke.

Some weeks later, at 3 a.m., the phone rang. It was Jill, calling from the States. 'Bryce, I've just sold the doorstop to an American publisher for six figures!' she yelled down the phone in excitement.

I was absolutely staggered somebody wanted to publish my manuscript. Now, twenty-three years later with *The Power of One* still in print the doorstop edition has reached a total of fifteen or so million copies and has been translated the world over. In 1992 it was made into a feature film directed by John Avildsen, and starring Stephen Dorff, John Gielgud, Morgan Freeman, Armin Mueller-Stahl and Daniel Craig. As they say in the classics, you never know until you give it a go.

Since *The Power of One* was published in 1989 I have written twenty-one books. Penguin Books, my brilliant publisher, recently announced that together we have achieved total sales of more than ten million books purchased by readers in my own country, and countless millions more around the world – both in English and in seventeen other languages, including Japanese and Chinese. What a huge thrill.

Throughout my writing life I have been mindful always that without readers, a writer doesn't amount to much. As Penguin prepares for the publication of this beautiful commemorative edition of *The Power of One*, may I use this occasion to thank you for your trust in me as a writer. In the ensuing twenty-three years since the brown and tattered doorstop was elevated into a worldwide bestseller it has been my pleasure and a privilege to entertain you.

FOREWORD TO THE COMMEMORATIVE EDITION

OF *THE POWER OF ONE*, OCTOBER 2012

'Dickens is my major influence. I think of myself as
a storyteller, so I tend to cherish the great storytellers:
John Steinbeck, Ernest Hemingway, Emile Zola,
Gabriel García Márquez, et al.'

SUNDAY TELEGRAPH, DECEMBER 2008

When I sat down I started writing about
what I knew. I'd had to pull myself up by the
bootstraps so I believe in the capacity of every
human being to triumph and to achieve anything.
But remember Peekay is larger than life,
as fictional characters need to be. So think
of it as the things that happened to me but
with a character better than I ever was.

'The accusation that I am a popular writer is one that I cherish enormously because the opposite is an unpopular writer.'

CANBERRA TIMES, NOVEMBER 1993

HOW TO WRITE A WORK
OF POPULAR FICTION

ONCE OR TWICE EACH YEAR for the past twenty years I have conducted what has become known as a masterclass teaching writers how to write a popular novel. Over this time I have conducted these classes in several countries, including Africa, Asia, America (Maui) – and, of course, at universities in Australia.

This year we have conducted two such classes at the National Library in Canberra. The course stretches over five days from 10 a.m. until 4.30 p.m. with at least four hours homework every night. Each class consists of an average of only twelve writers, though not necessarily published writers. The idea is to give people who are prepared to put in the long, hard, lonely hours at their desks at home a final nudge towards that grandest of all moments when they hold in their hands a story they have written that has been published. Or, in the future, they see it as an e-book with sales coming in from all over the world. Either way, for a writer, it is truly one of the great moments in life when someone unknown to you spontaneously and willingly reads and enjoys your work.

While it isn't quite the same thing as being part of a masterclass, I have put down what I believe and have practised over twenty-one books are the components of a popular novel. That is, those elements that should exist if a work of fiction is to appeal to a mass readership.

If you are a writer or aspiring writer you might like to consider the notes I leave with a class of writers after what is always an intensive week of writing. Let me say right off, these notes won't make you a great storyteller – that is a gift. But if you follow these guidelines and you have a good story to tell they will take you a fairly long way down the road to gaining a readership of your own. In the end, if you want to become a popular writer success is decided by readers and not by agents, publishers or critics.

I wish you luck, for without writers a country becomes mute and while the new social media is a revolution that has the potential to change the world, writers of honest, thoughtful and impassioned words in the process of telling a story will help to make the world free. When a country seeks to control what its writers say it inevitably becomes a dangerous and corrupted place. Viva le scribe.

As I have practised them, these then are the most important considerations in writing a work of popular fiction.

THE FOURTH PROTAGONIST

Although there may be a host of minor characters and lots of semi-important ones in a work of fiction, generally speaking there are three major characters who are likely to dominate your story or narrative, and we'll discuss them in particular under another headline later on.

However, to my mind there is a fourth character or protagonist – and that is the reader. She or he must be regarded as being a major part of your book. I shall refer to the reader as 'she' from here on, but of course I mean readers of both genders (although in most Western societies the majority of people who read fiction are women over the age of thirty-five). Should the book you're writing be essentially intended for males, then exactly the same rules apply. Simply substitute 'he' for 'she' as you read these directions.

She, the fourth protagonist, starts initially as a minor

character, in a sense playing a bit part to see if the action is to her liking. So it's up to one or all three of the main characters to prove she is about to undergo a significant experience. In other words, most readers venturing into a story by an author they don't regard as an old friend first knock on the front door. It's up to one or all of the major characters to get her into the hallway and into the kitchen to help with cooking up an exciting story – to become involved in the plot.

Once she is committed she brings an essential element into your fiction – she brings her experience, excitement, knowledge and speculation (future action). In other words, exactly the elements with which you have to equip your major characters to make them come alive on the page. Without a fourth protagonist or your reader, your book is incomplete. Or put more bluntly, if it ain't gonna be read by a lot of people it ain't any damn good as a work of popular fiction. So, don't neglect your reader, she is an essential character. Your reader also has an attribute your other characters don't possess – she can step out of the pages and tell others enthusiastically about the new characters, both good and bad, to be found in your book.

The fourth protagonist once she has agreed to take part will now refer to your book should it be temporarily misplaced, 'Has anyone seen my book?' Her sense of participation is what makes the difference. Write knowing who you want your fourth character to be. If you don't have a clear picture in your mind of who she is, it may be brilliant prose, a literary accomplishment, in fact, written with a quill from an angel's wing, but all it will end up being is a huge accomplishment. Somewhat like completing a very difficult jigsaw puzzle, you reward a great deal of personal gratification and delight or relief that you got all of the elements or pieces together. But then what? Almost inevitably the cat jumps onto the jigsaw tray and scatters the pieces beyond further interest. Rejection letters from publishers are never much fun to receive.

While you write, just as you keep your main characters topmost in your mind do the same for your reader, your fourth protagonist. She will reward you handsomely for giving her a place in your story.

DESCRIPTIVE NARRATIVE

In a writing class the first written assignment is titled: 'The sun rose in Africa'. I give class members half an hour to complete what is invariably around five hundred or so words of descriptive narrative.

I then call the writing to a halt and explain that in modern terms the reader has visually experienced being just about everywhere. We are now virtually in the third generation of colour TV, an age when telephones take pictures and send them together with text messages instantly around the neighbourhood, city or the world. Conversations across continents are practically composed of pictures, sound and immediate action. The scenic beauty of the planet we live in described so eloquently by writers in the pre-electronic age is now pretty redundant. We've all seen a hundred sunrises over Africa on TV or elsewhere on electronic media and so when spending words on the glorious happenstance of standing on the top of Mount Kilimanjaro one needs to be fairly selective. In other words, *only* describe what is essential to your storyline and is original information almost certainly unknown by your potential mass readership.

Of course, occasionally you will need to set a mood and this may require some careful description. But, as a general rule, go easy on the scenic wonder and leave the generally descriptive prose to the poets.

For example, should one of your characters be working in a kitchen it is not necessary to describe the environment. Most kitchens are pretty similar looking. The same applies with a hotel or restaurant kitchen, every reader has seen this cooking environment a hundred times in real life or on TV cooking programmes that seem to invade the air.

As a general rule, describe only what concerns the plot, that is, should the description be omitted the impact of the narrative will be lessened.

The urge to write endless descriptive narrative goes way back almost to kindergarten. It's hard-wired within most of us. It comes from times in centuries past when few people had travelled and books were the only journey they could make elsewhere. But somehow it has persisted even into the twenty-first century. Descriptive narrative was a good portion of any essay we wrote in the course of the ten or so years we spent going through primary and secondary school:

> As the sun rose a drop of silvery dew slid down the length of a stork of grass and landed with a bright splash on the back of a small brown snail getting ready for bed.
>
> *Teacher's note: Well done, Jessica! 9/10 – a stork is a bird. You mean, stalk. signed, Miss Forbes.*

Unnecessary descriptive narrative is a hard habit for a writer of fiction to give up. But ask yourself, is an elaborate and detailed setting essential to your story before you get down to the real action? Do you need it as a necessary element to get underway? Allow me to give you a somewhat exaggerated example of how to leave the non-essential descriptive narrative out while at the same time allowing the reader to supply her own imagined location details and the character in your story to get into the action.

The sun rose in Africa. For me another hot and pointless day spent in Morocco. God, why did I let myself in for this unmitigated disaster? How could I have possibly talked myself into travelling halfway across the globe to film a boxing match promoted by the International Association of Agnostics between three heavyweights, a Devout Muslim, Orthodox Jew and Charismatic Christian? Each supposedly chosen as the best fighter to represent their particular faith. The eventual winner to establish, once and for all, which of the three religions possesses the divine right to own God Himself? Christ! (Oops.) If the Muslim boxer doesn't win I'll probably be beheaded. No! Cancel that last thought or I could be accused of being a racist as well as being patently stupid.

As a freelance cameraman trying to earn a reputation with the US networks I've made some dumb decisions, but this one? Jesus! (Oops again!) To save costs I've spent a near-sleepless night in a bug-ridden hotel essentially intended for the less affluent among the locals. It is situated in a cheap quarter of a city I am soon to learn is notorious for its international drug trading.

Now, as a lone white guy holding a 35mm movie camera on the dirty narrow sidewalk, I suddenly have a sense of being very conspicuous. I spy a taxi and yell, gesticulate, wave madly, trying to compete with the honking, screeching, dodge-'em flow of vehicles that seems to be following no discernible set of traffic rules.

Success. The taxi turns sharply, dangerously, towards me and then its siren starts to blare. Holy Moses, it's a police car, the policeman in the passenger seat is pointing an AK 47 out of the window directly at me! I dodge behind a heap of garbage. Etc.

If the freelance cameraman is a main character we allow the reader to have immediate empathy and concern for what may happens to him. The scene, so briefly painted, allows the reader to enter the story and her own picture of the environment and then elect to get involved. The reader hasn't had to hack through several detailed paragraphs depicting the coming of the day in a largely Muslim African city.

Go easy on the pretty descriptive words. Always ask yourself, 'What does the fourth protagonist already know – or imagine she knows?' Allow her to bring her own descriptive detail into your storyline. *Only* show her what she doesn't know. Didactic self-indulgence using descriptive narrative is not a good characteristic for a popular fiction writer to possess.

REMOVE THE ADJECTIVES IN YOUR NARRATIVE PROSE

Perhaps you may be allowed one adjective in every chapter and only then because there is simply no better way of highlighting or describing something or someone. Over-employment of adjectives is often a sign of a novice writer or a lazy one. Try to think of adjectives as secondary words, because the trick is to show rather than tell your story. 'She was a fabulous person' tells you nothing. Similarly, 'They had a marvellous holiday!'

While I'm at it, watch those exclamation marks. One or two here and there in a book is sufficient. Of course, you may need many more in your dialogue, that is, if on occasion this is peppery or indicates a manner of speech. Adverbs should be watched as well – go easy on that stuff except of course in dialogue, because adverbs are common in the way most people talk.

It's not a bad idea to regularly go through your

narrative to see whether instead of the dreaded 'and' a plain old period (.) will do nicely. Thus making two sharp statements instead of possibly one languid sentence.

CHARACTER IS PLOT

As a writer nothing resonates more clearly with me than the words above this sentence. What the character says and does will determine the direction your story takes.

We all respond to stimulus differently. In other words we see events and feel emotions as individuals. Two people may see the same incident and react to it quite differently. While this response to stimulus often changes with age, how we interpret what we see and feel as adults has a great deal to do with our home environment, religion, societal and national backgrounds. This is not a new thought, but I am constantly dismayed that writers think that a storyline or plot is separate from the characters they bring to the plot to make it work. The plot (or stimulus) cannot take place without the interpretation the characters bring to it. Their backgrounds will determine how the story tells.

It then stands to reason that you, as a writer, must know your main characters at a very intimate level when you bring them into your narrative. The trick is to allow this knowledge to leak out gradually, so that your reader is intrigued and surprised as she gets to know them. If the characters react to stimulus in a way surprising to the reader's own background then she must be able to eventually or immediately reconcile her reaction to the character(s) background as you the writer has evolved it to this point in your book.

In other words, the characters in your book – especially the three major ones – are the instruments with which you have to work. It is they who create the originality in your storyline. After all, not that many original stories exist – most involve universal emotions such as love, hate, greed, envy, joy, sorrow or despair. It is your job to use these elements to produce intrigue, laughter, tears and original outcomes that satisfy the reader.

It is for this reason that most storylines involve roughly the same culture as the reader. The great storytellers are those among us who can evolve a character(s) that may possess many alien characteristics that, in the course of events, are understood and enjoyed by readers from many different cultures. By the way, the movies and TV have played an important part in this cultural cross-referencing. Once again we see the role of the fourth protagonist and what she brings as a character into your book.

However, until you know your major characters very well indeed – so that you can manipulate and play with them while maintaining their essential personalities – it is difficult to make them convincing in your storyline or plot. As a writer, once I have an idea for a book I build the personalities of my usually three major characters months before I start to write. I usually steal bits and pieces from different people I know, who I imagine may fit into the environment in which I am writing. Moreover, it is difficult to keep bits of yourself and your own experience out of a character's personality. Know your main characters sufficiently well before you start to write to be able to conduct an imaginary conversation with them on a topic of mutual interest.

Of course you can have more than three major characters in a book, but it's not a bad idea to include three that last the distance – that is, from when you introduce them until the end, or near the end of your story. You will, of course, have multiple 'walk-ons' as characters and others that stay somewhat longer – weekend guests so to speak. But let your fourth protagonist be on intimate terms with your major characters so that she has firm opinions about them even though they are going to constantly surprise her as you reveal the different layers to each with regard to their background, motivations, beliefs and all the other influences that go into making an individual totally believable.

Remember, for a character to work well he or she should be just a little larger than life so that they jump off the page rather than get buried in the pulp or lost on the screen. In other words, they react to the stimulus you throw at them with a little more impact or derring-do than your reader might if she were undergoing the same circumstances. Don't go overboard. Superman or woman belongs to the comic books. Just give them a little more impact in a given situation than perhaps someone may create in a similar situation in real life. Not only in triumph but also in disaster.

USING DIALOGUE, VERSUS STRAIGHT NARRATIVE, TO TELL A STORY

When your characters speak they tell you much more than what they happen to be saying. 'Show me, don't tell me' is an important aspect of storytelling, perhaps the most important instruction of them all. The author telling the reader what happened versus the characters speaking to allow the plot or storyline to unfold is often the difference between a good book and a mediocre one.

The Ndebele tribe in Africa have a saying: *People are people because of other people.* In other words, we understand each other by observing those people around us, how they behave and speak. We make decisions about ourselves and about others by how they employ language – the words they use and the meanings they imply tell us their status or lack of standing they enjoy or suffer in our or their society.

'He badly needs a good kick up the arse' comes from a very different individual than 'I say, old chap, may I say that's going rather too far.' Or, 'Mate, do that again and I'll bust your teeth in!' Or 'You're a disgrace! I don't know what's come over you lately, but as your mum I'm ashamed of you.' As opposed to 'Darling, you've disgraced us all by your atrocious behaviour.' Or, 'Righto, that's enough, no more ya hear or I'm gunna tell ya father – and if I do he'll beat the crap outta ya!'

I urge you to look at your narrative flow and where you can change description of the action into interactive dialogue. This is so the reader can judge the situation by how it is affecting the characters personally rather than by being told by the writer how the characters are affected by the situation in which they find themselves.

Of course, you need both straight narrative prose and dialogue in a work of fiction. But good dialogue brings immediacy into your storyline, brings it alive. One character speaking to another is much more immediate and impactful than if the situation is described in straight prose.

Make a habit of listening to how the people around you talk. How they make decisions based on their social demographics. If possible, see how close you can get to their background. Most good writers are also listeners and hear not only what is said, but also what remains unsaid. Remember, dialogue doesn't only emerge from lips but is also compounded and emphasised by gesture and expression.

POINT OF VIEW (POV)

You will have come across this before. Almost every writing workshop will emphasise the importance of point of view (POV). Your character should not be ambivalent, but instead should possess an unambiguous point of view, often a very definite one. The writer should be aware of this at all times and while people seldom change their point of view in life, it is common enough in writing where the storyline has as its singular or as one of its purposes to have one character persuade another to change. Or perhaps the experience the characters undergo leads them to change their point of view. The quest for happiness, power, wealth or respect is a common theme in storytelling. The changes your character may have to undertake to achieve whichever of these ambitions is your storyline.

Metamorphosis and the clash of two or more points of view is a common enough theme in fiction, but it can't take place effectively unless the writer allows the reader to agree to the character change, or at least understand and accept it as valid.

Of course, you may have a character with no real point of view – although I recommend you use him or her sparingly. We've all experienced a new guest to dinner or over a prolonged situation who answers your numerous questions with monosyllabic replies, then, to make matters more difficult, doesn't seem the least curious about you and asks you no questions in return. It's hard work in real life and it's hard work in fiction – except perhaps in a situation meant to be humorous. To begin to know your characters intimately you need to know their point of view and how they acquired it.

THE USE OF COINCIDENCE

Okay, maybe you can use an act of coincidence *once* in your book. That is, if you have a sufficiently good reason to do so. But NEVER use it to get yourself or your characters out of trouble. When you do so it becomes lazy writing. When your character finds himself or herself in a predicament it's your job to work them out of it – no sudden unexpected rescue mission out of the blue, no verbal helicopter plucking them out of the jungle to free them from their terrorist captors.

KEEPING THE BOAT IN THE CENTRE OF THE RIVER

I find it helpful to think of a story as a boat on its journey from the mountains to the sea – the beginning of the narrative flow to the end of your story. Once in a while the story-boat becomes stranded in the marshes instead of remaining where the stream flows fastest in the middle of the river.

We have all on occasions made the error of falling in love with a subject or with our own expertise, and telling the reader much more than she needs to know for the story to progress. In other words, the story-boat (narrative flow) becomes diverted from the mainstream and flounders in the dreaded marshes situated every little while along the riverbank.

These stretches of marshes are simply where the writer is showing off or becoming personally fascinated with subject matter beyond the interest of the reader, rather than giving the reader the continuity of storyline she needs to remain interested in the outcome. Keep the story-boat in the fast-running water, the centre of the stream, so as to drive it as fast as possible downstream to the sea, the conclusion of your story.

Should your story take place in two time frames, possibly centuries apart, tell the story in three parts – book one, the situation in the past, book two, the situation in the present and book three, the reconciliation of the two periods to bring it to conclusion. Don't try to be too clever, keep it simple.

Alternatively, if the chapters past and present are running parallel, make sure the connections get made between each chapter so that the present and past characters don't get lost but remain clearly defined and are given more or less equal emphasis so the reader can follow the storyline without difficulty.

BEWARE OF SENDING MESSAGES

As a writer or would-be writer of popular fiction, beware of becoming the writer with a cause, a burning desire to persuade the world that your message is the only one and your point of view the correct one. While you may write a book with a strong theme, your job is not to deliver messages but to write so that the reader is persuaded that she has reached her own conclusion and not your didactic message. This can only be achieved if you give both sides of a viewpoint – best done with dialogue to be convincing. Coming directly from the author makes it tricky – your true colours are likely to show. Have a main character representing each side. For instance, in the long-running conflict between Israel and Palestine don't write simply one or the other's point of view. Remember always, you are a storyteller. As the great Yiddish writer Isaac Bashevis Singer once said, 'If you want messages go to Western Union.'

RESEARCHING TIME, PLACE AND INCIDENT

Every story takes place somewhere and wherever that is you must make sure you know the location, historical period and culture accurately. Don't guess. While you may create an incident or a story that never happened, where and how and the reactions of the people at the time to the incident or story must be believable. The social and political environment, tools used, common beliefs, education, dress, food, customs, in particular language construction, common slang and argot, social differences and dialogue must be accurate. You owe it to your reader or fourth protagonist to take her into a world that truly existed. Make one major mistake and your reader will being to doubt the veracity of some of the other facts in your writing. Tiny things count – for instance, don't have a character changing blades in a razor before the safety razor was invented. In my first novel, *The Power of One*, I had a major character use his beloved Hasselblad camera shortly before it was invented. I received over a thousand letters worldwide correcting me, including one from the Swedish manufacturer begging me to nevertheless retain it in the novel.

Stick to the verifiable facts unless, of course, you are writing fantasy, but it's as well to be careful with this genre also and remain consistent in all of the usual societal concerns, even if your 'take place' is in an imagined world.

THE SUSPENSION OF DISBELIEF

There is a phenomenon that takes place with the fourth protagonist or reader when she enters your book in that she temporarily suspends her critical analysis and takes you at your word. She accepts your larger-than-life characters and inwardly agrees it's your story and she goes along with it and even becomes a part of it. But if you state something she knows to be inaccurate or impossible at the time in which you are writing then the invisible band that connects her to your narrative snaps. This suspension of disbelief is critical to maintain if you are to enjoy a relationship with your reader, so be careful with your facts – if they can be checked then you *must* do your homework.

Tension – keeping your prose tight and your action moving forward – is essential in writing for a popular audience. We talked earlier about the dreaded marshlands and the story-boat but this is even further caution. You are writing popular fiction and you will only endure if it remains that way. Few things are less popular than a book that is self-indulgent and meanders ever onwards.

To my mind every chapter, short or long, should contain sufficient of your story to be a story in its own right – almost a complete passage with a beginning, middle and end. But it has to be more than this. Each chapter must build excitement and tension or 'want to know' by the reader so that she feels compelled to continue.

Here is a mnemonic I have evolved to illustrate the manner and flow or momentum of a popular novel: the saw on its back, teeth facing upwards, with each cutting edge a chapter and consecutively rising a fraction higher – in other words, bringing more tension to bear until the last big cut when the story ends.

I have termed this tension that resolves at the very top of the saw-tooth – or end of the chapter – as 'relevant surprise'. It's where the reader learns something about the character or story she didn't anticipate and could never have guessed would occur – something that drives the story onwards in an unexpected though relevant way. 'Wow! I'd never have guessed that was going to happen' is what you hope the reader will be saying inwardly as she reaches the end of each chapter.

Usually, but not always, this *relevant surprise* factor will be where you begin the next chapter. Yes, it's hard to do, but it's also excellent to dare your genius to walk the wildest unknown way. Unpredictability is often one of the more important reasons why we read books. Witness the huge popularity of crime novels that almost exclusively deal in a storyline intended to keep the reader guessing the outcome. Also, by the way, many crime writers persist in using a larger-than-life major character previously known to the reader in every book they write. It's been going sufficiently long now for it not to be a fluke – a character the reader knows and loves and who will keep her guessing until the very end. Witness Sherlock Holmes and Miss Marple and a host of others who have lasted more than a century.

So, don't make the mistake of thinking that relevant surprise doesn't belong to the genre in which you are writing. In fact it could be said, along with 'character is plot' to be the very essence of storytelling and your work of fiction is unlikely to be an exception.

Keep the tension going and work out the twists and turns every good character undergoes and also the quirks of personality that cause them to do or undertake relevant but surprising-to-the-reader events.

As a possible tip that may be helpful to you, before I start writing, in evolving my relevant surprise factor, I often take the chapter I'm writing to my daily twenty-minute thinking session. You may wish to try this method, sit quietly somewhere, though not necessarily at your desk, and think exclusively about your storyline and chapter conclusion. Isolating a writing problem from the thought clutter of everyday life can have surprising results.

BUM GLUE

Writing is about practice, and practice takes time. I call this 'bum glue' – that is, time spent writing. Life is a busy process and sometimes we 'back boiler' the things that, to complete the metaphor, should be allowed to go 'full steam ahead'. If you are going to be a successful writer you have to allocate time to your manuscript. Practice and more practice is a process that never stops, but thankfully it is always rewarding in the end. This is because writing requires thinking at a deeper level than most things, and most writers find that they grow intellectually in the process of writing.

As humans we were given the gift of speech and with it came the gift of imagination. We are able to imagine new horizons, new developments and then attempt to visit them or bring them about. Without imagination we'd still be grunting at each other clothed in animal skins and living in a cave.

As a writer the gift of imagination and the insights that come with it are especially important. If you dedicate time to your writing you will become a deeper thinker – the how, why, when and where of the process we refer to as being completely alive becomes more easily understood. You are now a storyteller. It is your job to explain to the rest of us who we are, where we came from and where we might be going. Dare I say it, but writing, hard as it is, has its own reward.

Allocate the time to practise your writing. In so far as it is possible, be consistent with this time frame and don't let anything or anyone take priority. Give your writing as much time as you can possibly scrape together in a busy life. Not a few moments here and there but a considered time you allocate each week when you apply bum glue and get down to writing.

I must warn you, although I'm sure your own experience has taught you, that writing is among the most difficult things you will ever undertake. Difficult tasks require time and thought and the more of both you give them the easier they become.

However, writing is a task that is never really easy. This is because there is no limit to where it can take you and unlike a mountain, you will never reach the top. On every occasion after placing the last period onto the final page of a novel I say to myself, 'This time they are going to find out I'm no good.' We write because we have to or love to or, more than anything else, want to – and thank God we do. Without artists, writers, singers, dancers, actors the world would be a sorry place. But remember, the first words in the Big Book, 'In the beginning was the word.'

'I AM A WRITER'

Repeat this as a mantra last thing before you fall asleep and the moment you wake up in the morning. We all know the human brain responds to repetition and if you're prepared to put in the work you will surely get the desired result.

But no disclaimers or prefacing. 'I am a writer' – nothing less. When you sit down to glue your bum to your writing chair this *must* be your mindset.

Good luck and *never* give up.

'Finally, the first copy arrives and you hold it and you open it, and almost the moment you open it up there's a flap of the covers and the bird flies away. It's not yours any more, it's gone, and it becomes somebody else's.'

HERALD SUN, NOVEMBER 2004

Damon died in my arms. And so like everybody,
we have tragedy in our lives. And so yes,
there is tragedy in [April Fool's Day] *too —*
there are all the emotions.

'I'm a character-driven novelist and I'm fascinated by the human persona and the travails and troubles and angst and adventures that we human beings manage to create for ourselves . . . I'm driven to tell stories. Stories absolutely fascinate me, and while writing is a hard process, I can't conceive of not doing it. It is a compulsive and impulsive thing.'

THE MERCURY, DECEMBER 1997

THE THING THAT
MAKES ME HAPPIEST

THE THING THAT MAKES ME HAPPIEST in life is growing something. I still marvel at the fact I can bury a bulb in soil and it will transform into something so beautiful. If you look in my greenhouse right now you'll see all the summer vegetables we're going to eat. I've sowed the seedlings, they're up, they're in there, and in about three or four weeks time I will transplant them to my garden and watch them grow. Soon, they will feed us.

I've made the soil from mulch. Everything we eat in this house goes into a bin and gets turned into soil. Every leaf that falls off the trees in the garden has been collected and gets turned into soil so that I'm in this process of turning everything over – the soil of my garden has been made by the food that we've eaten, and by the skins of oranges and by the leaves that fell off the trees in autumn. And then to watch something grow, this miracle of growth! Right now if you look into the garden you can see the daffodils, but I can remember selecting the bulbs and spending hours sowing them. And if you look in about three weeks time, the tulips will start coming out, and then the pansies for spring. For me that is just a miracle – the growth, the business of starting.

And children are the same. Children are miracles to me. See a small child growing, he has a point of view, and this small boy is gonna be, one day, something special – who knows. Growth. The business of growing up, and growing up properly, fascinates me. So plants for me are everything.

EXCERPT FROM PENGUIN TV INTERVIEW
WITH BRYCE COURTENAY, 2012

'You live three lives. One growing up; one being responsible, paying your mortgage and having kids; and one being yourself. I'm now in my third stage.'

SUNDAY AGE, DECEMBER 1989

'I believe in magic. Magic and imagination are the same thing. When we take the imagination out of the human we reduce them to only what is known, not what could be, and a human being operating only in the known is always unfortunate.'

THE MERCURY, FEBRUARY 1997

TAP-DANCING FACTS

ON MY SEVENTIETH BIRTHDAY, all my mates had coffee together and I said, 'Fellas, I've got a present for you, I've got a present for you. I'm going to stop, this is my seventieth birthday, I'm going to stop bullshitting!'

And they all went, 'No, no! Don't do that! That would destroy everything, that would mess up everything! No, no, no, NO!'

Now I don't know where you take it from there.

I've been called a liar, I've been called a bullshit artist, I've been called all of those things. I *am* a storyteller and I'm not sure that some of it isn't fair comment in the sense that it is very difficult for me to look a fact in the eye and see it, like a small naked actual fact. I like to put a sort of top hat on a fact and dress him in a silk shirt and a pair of striped pants and a couple of tap shoes and then let him do a bit of a tap dance. I am liable to take facts and dress them up and make them work for me.

And perhaps, you know, if you're being kind you'd call it storytelling and if you want to be crude, if you want to be rude and if you want to be nasty you'd call it bullshitting – and it may in fact be an amalgam of both. But the point is it is very hard for me to look a naked fact in the eye and not want to do something with it – with that fact.

Because nothing I was taught – I mean nothing! – nothing I was taught at school has proved to be true. The atom was supposed to be the smallest thing that ever existed. We know the quark is smaller. Every single scientific fact, every thing that people said 'This is the definite truth' about has been proved to be bullshit and it has proved to be different.

And two people watching the same car accident have a totally different recall of what happened, so if storytellers didn't make facts tap dance then where would we be? I mean we'd all be looking at each other trying to think of some sort of undressed, tiny, small quivering truth and yes, there are truths you have to tell, but I think I can say in my defence, I have never told a story – or, to put it crudely, bullshitted – to hurt anybody or to gain anything from it, or to get richer, or to impress anybody. I've done it for the sake of the story. For me the story is everything, and sometimes one translation of the story isn't another person's translation. And sometimes I *hear* my mates say, 'Oh, shit – here we go, kid' as I extrapolate on something. But I know they love it – *they love it*, because it makes the fact *dance,* and *dancing facts are what it's all about.* If we lived life factually, as exactly as it's supposed to be – as the Roman Catholic priest, or the Anglican minister or the Buddhist tells you it has to be – God, wouldn't it be miserable?!

All I know is, I don't know any other way.

EXCERPT FROM PENGUIN TV INTERVIEW

WITH BRYCE COURTENAY, 2012

'I have a real sense of life. I believe there are three precepts in life, which most people don't understand and I understand extraordinarily well. Number one: that somebody has to do it and it might as well be me. Number two: I have an incredible tenacity, I never give up, and perseverance is everything to me. If everyone else is lying in the gutter saying we can't go any further, if only by sticking my tongue out I will. And number three: just hang in there. I am the original realist. I don't expect anything from anybody. Life is tough, I know it's rough and I don't expect any thanks.'

MELBOURNE WEEKLY, JUNE 1997

Music has played a huge part in my life,
a huge part in the sense that as a small child
in the orphanage the African people who
ran the orphanage were a musical people.
So when I was miserable and things were just
too awful for words, there was always music
around. Later on I got more sophisticated,
and I became a bit of a jazz nut and then into
classical music . . . Music is the stuff of life.

'We should share each other's music because music has only harmony. It gives us life, it gives us vigour, it gives us movement, we treasure it, it gives us memories – it gives us everything.'

EXCERPT FROM PENGUIN TV INTERVIEW
WITH BRYCE COURTENAY, 2012

MUSIC

AS I HAVE NO FAMILY BACKGROUND concerning music, it has largely been a voyage of self-discovery. I have a fairly eclectic taste and nothing you could call highbrow. But what little I know has given me a great deal of pleasure and I write with classical music playing on the radio all day.

I first discovered Beethoven, Verdi and Wagner when I was working in high explosives underground in the Rhone Antelope Copper Mines in what is now known as Zambia, then Northern Rhodesia. The detritus of the world washed up there, ex-Nazi SS troops and officers, the scum of the earth. It was a dangerous job, but I needed the money for university in England. And it gave me an enormous lust for life; every night I faced the prospect of not coming out alive, but it paid handsomely. What you could earn in three or four years somewhere else, I could earn in a year.

I was staying in the singles quarters, which was unofficially run by a bunch of former Nazi SS who had escaped from Germany after the war and, like so many other ingrates and misfits, had come to Central Africa where questions as to your background remained unasked. They were a bunch of thugs, but one or two of them loved Beethoven and Wagner and I'd hear this music coming from their quarters. I liked what I heard and so started searching for more, eventually discovering Brahms, Bruch, Bach and many, many others. Classical music has since become a lifetime passion. Along the way I also discovered and grew to love jazz. And then of course the Beatles and Bob Dylan – and I'll even admit to loving some of the earlier country and western.

Throughout *Jack of Diamonds* I've weaved some of my favourite pieces of music and for a little bit of fun, even had Jack meet up with some of my favourite performers! Hope you enjoy discovering these musical references and that you also find beauty and inspiration, peace and solace in music – which has the capacity to enrich our very existence.

EXCERPT FROM PENGUIN TV INTERVIEW
WITH BRYCE COURTENAY, 2012

People think life is an opportunity to take things out but not to put back. I've discovered that if you want to get to the real essence, you have to put in more than you take out.

'History so frequently repeats itself. Almost every human endeavour has an antecedent and you realise why something has happened. Finding those reasons are, for me, the whole purpose of writing.'

NEWCASTLE HERALD, NOVEMBER 2006

THE UNFORTUNATE
PROCESS OF DYING SLOWLY

I FIND MYSELF IN THE UNFORTUNATE PROCESS of slowly dying. I don't mean the way we all are, each day twenty-four hours nearer to the ultimate demise, but slowly, because I have a fairly accurate use-by date – in fact, a matter of months to live.

A sudden death at old age, for instance a heart attack, has the disadvantage of not being able to say farewell to those you love. On the other hand, given always that you've reached a ripe old age, it means those who were obliged to care for you can get over the grieving process and get on with their lives while keeping, one hopes, the sweet thoughts about time spent together and happily discarding the negative ones.

In my case I have a wife who can look forward to another quarter of a century of good life and I simply hate the idea of her having to use some of that precious time processing my dying. Of course, my greatest desire would be to remain intellectually viable and physically capable until the very last moment when I finally shut my eyes, my last thought being that I have enjoyed a vastly fortunate life, and die in the presence of a woman I love with all my heart.

While I don't wish to dwell on the circumstances of my birth, a quick reprise. I was born illegitimately and to a single mother and placed in an orphanage at three months – at the time a quite common circumstance for unmarried women without ongoing and committed male partners. I was born in 1933 almost plumb in the centre of the Great Depression, when the financial world was in freefall and no government could even contemplate social or financial help for a woman finding herself single and with a child – in fact, in my mother's case two children. The orphanages in South Africa were crowded with such children.

I was then taken out and returned on several occasions to various institutions as my mother attempted and failed to make a home for my sister Rosemary and myself. Quite how many times we shuffled from one institution to another I can't say, as I was too young to recall most of them. Finally at around seven I was removed from the

Boys Hostel in a small town aptly named Duiwelskloof (Devil's Canyon) in rural Northern Transvaal. From here I returned to my mother's childhood home where my mother took care of my grandfather in a small town in the Eastern Transvaal named Barberton.

My mother was a dressmaker – not a good vocation when nobody could afford to purchase clothes. I guess we were poor, although the term 'socially deprived' had probably not yet been coined and anyway, it didn't seem of importance as society had only just survived the bumpy ride of the Great Depression and World War II had commenced.

At the age of seven or eight and back with my mother and grandfather I can't recall ever feeling deprived. In a small town kids are all equal and the boys all went around barefooted wearing a pair of khaki shorts and a shirt (no underpants), even for school and, more importantly, even to meet God at Sunday school. You could always tell the poorer girls as they seldom wore a ribbon in their hair (only to Sunday school) and their plaits were tied with two small pieces of twine, rubber bands being unavailable due to the war effort.

It used to be thought that what happens in the first seven years of a child's life will vastly influence its remainder. I only make these early years known to point out that the presumption that difficult circumstances in early life, rather than leading to an unfortunate outcome, have in my case led to a most fortunate one. There's nothing quite like starting on the bottom rung of the social ladder and then learning to recognise each rung as you attempt to step ever upwards. I have always thought that kids raised with parents placed somewhere on the middle or upper range of the social ladder must find it difficult to know in what direction their lives are headed.

However, let me hasten to say, my beginning involved placing a toe on the bottom rung of a white man's ladder and not that of the black man. My most fortunate of all circumstances was that in the year 1933 when I was born I commenced life possessing a white skin and blue eyes. In the South Africa of that time I was already racially miles ahead in the process of growing to an elevated adulthood.

Now back to dying and how it feels to be doing so over a protracted period of some months. I guess I might be expected to look back in regret at the mistakes I have made which, to say the least, have been numerous. Then again, we only learn by making mistakes of commission, so inevitably, provided always we accept and act upon the lessons learned, errors of judgement are essential in the progression of any life.

To my mind, this is why starting at the bottom rung is so beneficial. Decisions made are seldom ambiguous – they either benefit or detract from the process of individual happiness, loving, fulfilment, duty, creativity and, finally, ambition of the kind that doesn't need to attach itself to power over others or greed. All of these six desirable happenstances are, in my opinion, singularly and collectively the correct reasons for making any decision.

With regard to the aggregation of all six human endeavours, I count myself most fortunate as I can truly say that in the process of climbing the ladder of life I have enjoyed my fair share and more of all six. Hence, the certain knowledge that I am dying is no reason to bemoan the impending circumstance.

There is yet another instance where I count myself extremely fortunate. While I love my country I have never had to fight for the collective ideals of its agreements with other kindred nations. I have missed, by a matter of a few years, every war in which both my country of birth and that of my adoption have been involved. I have never known the horror it must be to kill another man for so-called ideological reasons. This, even though the justification and propaganda at the time will no doubt have correctly or incorrectly convinced my side that as we were without question the righteous and the just and it was therefore our duty to extinguish the enemy's fiery ideology or ambitions.

I read somewhere that seven out of every ten humans murdered in the past 2000 years in the name of religion have been at the hands of the Christian faith. If correct and given the conviction that ours is the sword of righteousness, this is a sobering thought. We emphatically believe we have invariably been on the side of justice and peace and have always been the ones to espouse interracial, ideological and religious fraternity. While I am tainted by the sins of the past, I have been rewarded by not having to become physically involved in any of these conflicts of self-interest by having to put my young life on the firing line. I have always maintained that nations should only send men over fifty years of age to war. If we did this, I feel sure there would be far less conflict in the world. Old men make the decisions and send the flower of their youth to die in the name of one or another ideology, faith or territorial or greedy ambition.

Enough of my indulgent rambling on – time to return to the curiosity of dying over a roughly measurable prognosis. For the first time I am experiencing on a daily basis the 'never again' feeling. That is, sensing that some task or experience will never again occur in one's life. It is a distinctly unique physical and mental catharsis, like the sudden automatic application of brakes to avoid an accident.

Together with being a writer I am also a very keen gardener. In fact, if the act of tilling the soil and growing beautiful and practical plants had been removed from my life I would have been immeasurably the poorer for this. Sowing, then seeing a tiny seedling peep out of the soil then, busting with fecundity come into bloom or eatable adulthood, then slowly commence the return circle back to seed, is to me the daily, monthly and seasonal miracle to which most people seem oblivious. For goodness sake, I even admire the tenacity of so-called weeds.

As I write, spring is just about done and summer about to commence. My spring flowering is returning to seed, the daffs slipping back into their long two-seasonal slumber. This year the tulips will have to remain underground together with the daffodil bulbs. Alas, if I should raise them ready for replanting again in autumn, I'm not sure they will be returned to the soil. Non-gardeners have the misfortune of having stressful matters on their minds.

Now as I transplant the seedling from the greenhouse into the warming, soon-to-be summer soil, I get this pervasive 'never again' feeling, knowing that I am unlikely to eat from the veggie patch or see the seedlings I'm propagating come into bloom. Of all the 'never agains' this is for me one of the most poignant.

Years ago, while in the United Kingdom and strolling

through Sherwood Forest paying homage to my childhood enchantment with Robin Hood and his band of merry men, I stooped and pocketed a single acorn. On my return to Australia it lay long forgotten in a desk drawer to be discovered some nine years ago after I had decided to move to a lovely valley on the Central Coast where it was my intention to build a ten-acre garden on its only eyesore, a site that had been completely destroyed of its natural vegetation by a long-since-abandoned brick- and earthworks.

My idea being to demonstrate that no matter how inhospitable the land may appear, with sufficient love and care and a bit of knowledge it can be returned to its former natural condition. My intention was to grow only native plants. But with the now some forty-years-old acorn in my pocket I thought to myself, 'What the hell?' With no expectations I planted it as well. You can guess the rest.

The land restoration took some five years to complete and I left a still young but almost fully restored landscape to move to the Southern Highlands and a lovely home with a thirty-five-year-old beautiful garden, taking the five-year-old oak tree with me.

After three years we moved to Canberra and this week the new owners take over the property in Bowral. That is, they move in without my 'Robin Hood oak' now some ten feet or three-and-a-half metres tall. In two days it will be planted in the backyard of our Canberra home and yes, I will never see it drop its leaves in autumn, face the winter cold, observe its cheery budding in the spring and green-leafed and optimistic throw of summer shade as it sets about the hundred-year task of from a single acorn growing into a mighty oak.

It's been a lovely journey. At six I suffered from a bout of tonsillitis and the local town doctor decided he would take me to Pietersburg, a larger town some seventy miles further north where the facilities existed to operate and remove my tonsils. His name was Dr Hennie Venter and he owned a chocolate-brown 1939 Chevrolet with a dicky-seat at the back where the boot is usually to be found. Instead of the boot you withdrew a seat into the open air. To my immense joy he allowed me to ride in the dicky-seat all the way to the hospital.

As a small five-year-old child bullied mercilessly in the Boys Hostel I simply couldn't imagine any person wealthy enough to own such a splendid carriage, and on my dicky-seated return two weeks later, upon arriving at the Boys Hostel, I plucked up the courage to ask Dr Venter, 'Sir what must I do to become as rich as you?'

I recall his laughter and then his reply, 'Son, the greatest helping hands you will ever possess are attached to the ends of your wrists.'

This was my first incentive to reach out and grab the bottom rung of the ladder, then the second, until finally, now at the age of seventy-nine, I stand remarkably at what I perceive to be the last rung. By this I mean I have achieved all I set out to do. I hasten to add I have enjoyed a good deal of help and good fortune brought about by the wisdom and generosity of friends I have known and loved. I have possessed more in every one of the six human endeavours than I could possibly have deserved. My life is completed.

However, there remains only one further ambition, or rather it would appear, one exception to total fulfilment. Now that my use-by date is almost upon me my last remaining ambition, though I am discovering it is an Australia-wide bureaucratically imposed impossibility, is to be buried vertically in a cardboard box and then have a ghost gum planted over me. No tombstone, no name plaque, no given place except a place in the Australian bush of sunshine and cold, wild wind and calm, where fire renews growth, somewhere natural where my flesh and bones might be useful to the eternal renewal of life.

Now, wouldn't that be a way to go – there grows the ghost gum of Bryce Courtenay.

You know darling, I've just been out in my garden. The garden looks lovely but then you get this feeling that I will never see this plant bloom. It's a weird sort of feeling to be thinking these things. It's not mawkish, but just that as you go about doing things, planting things, that you are doing so 'for the last time'.

'We have to spend more time educating our kids to do something more than destroying our wilderness for money. And we need to start in our own backyard. We say we're a nation who tread lightly upon the earth, but we're not, and that is a great shame.'

AUSTRALASIAN POST, JANUARY 2001

The Editor,
The Canberra Times,
10th November 2012

Dear Editor,

*Together with the enclosed this may appear to be one
of the more unusual letters you receive this week and
certainly an explanation is necessary.*

*Some twenty-four years ago I was given, as part
of a winter promotion by your newspaper, a sloppy
joe inscribed with your logo. At the time I was the
creative director of Patterson Bates Advertising.
As it happened this was the winter in which I wrote*
The Power of One *and I wore your sloppy joe with
every page completed. With the surprising success of
my first novel I continued to wear it every winter for
the next twenty-one novels, coming to believe that
without it I couldn't possibly write a bestseller.*

*Twenty-one number-one bestsellers in twenty-
three years and some twenty-five million books in
twenty-eight languages later, I have written my last
book, and in several months my 'Use-by date' will
arrive and, at the risk of mixing my metaphors,*

I am in the process of sweeping the autumnal leaves from Memory Lane.

It occurred to me that you might like to have the sloppy joe? Perhaps an arrogant thought? If so, please dispatch it to the garbage bin. I simply wanted you to know that superstition is alive and well and that I am grateful to you for a promotional gift that may well be the longest surviving garment ever given away by a newspaper. The fact that it has survived in constant use for so long is a testimony to both its quality and also that of the newspaper who gave it to me. I apologise for the disrepair and the darning – somehow, apart from dry-cleaning, it didn't seem right to attempt to tart it up.

Enclosed is a signed preview copy of my latest – and final – book.

Yours sincerely,
Bryce Courtenay

Strictly as somebody who gave somebody ten
minutes' entertainment, perhaps last thing at
night. That would be a wonderful memory.
'He gave me ten minutes of my day for twenty
years' — and what a compliment that would be.
I could never deserve a compliment like that
but that's the one I'd love most —
just ten minutes a day.

'I take my friendships seriously; they are enormously important to me – in the end your mates are your life.'

SUNDAY AGE, DECEMBER 2005

I've had a wonderful life, but part of that
wonderful life has been those people who've been
kind enough to pick up a Bryce Courtenay book,
and read it, and enjoy it, and buy the next one,
and be with me on what has been, for me,
an incredible journey. And all I'd like to say is,
as simply as I possibly can, thank you.
Thank you, thank you, thank you.

'I am a storyteller. Some people are plumbers,
some people are doctors, some are lawyers.
I'm a storyteller.'

THE AGE, APRIL 1993

AND GOD CREATED A FLOWER
AND NAMED IT AFTER THE SUN

YOU POSSIBLY HAVEN'T GIVEN a great deal of thought to that most unpretentious flower of them all – the sunflower. She's big, clumsy-looking, open, surprisingly shy and modest – a thoroughly nice girl who doesn't expect to be noticed at a party along with the roses, tulips, daffs and other female exotica.

Never truly a wallflower, she always helps clear up afterwards and can usually be found up to her elbows in soap suds laughing and cheerful as she does the dishes while the other girls find dark corners to giggle and cuddle with their boyfriends.

However, take a closer look. Big, yes, but the smile never leaves her face. Look into it and you see the pure simplicity that is genuine beauty, the personification of the sun itself.

I beg you, this year plant a single sunflower seed preferably in your front garden in a part that receives lots of sunlight. Then watch what happens when Miss Sunflower grows tall, smiling, facing the sun and happily greets everyone who passes by.